The children were outside. They were
playing football.

Wilf kicked the ball. It landed in
a bush.

"Sorry," said Wilf.

Wilf couldn't get the ball.

"I can get it," said Kipper.

Kipper found a case.

"Look at this," he said. "I found it in the bush."

Dad looked at the case.

He couldn't open it.

Wilf looked at the case.

"What can be in it?" he asked. "It looks important."

"What is in it?" asked Wilma.

"I don't know," said Chip, "but it
looks very important."

"What is in the case?" asked Kipper.

"I don't know," said Biff, "but it looks very, very important."

"What is in this case?" asked Dad.

"We don't know," said the police
officer, "but it is very important."

A man came in a big car.
"Who is he?" asked Kipper.

"I don't know," said Dad, "but he looks important."

The man took the case.

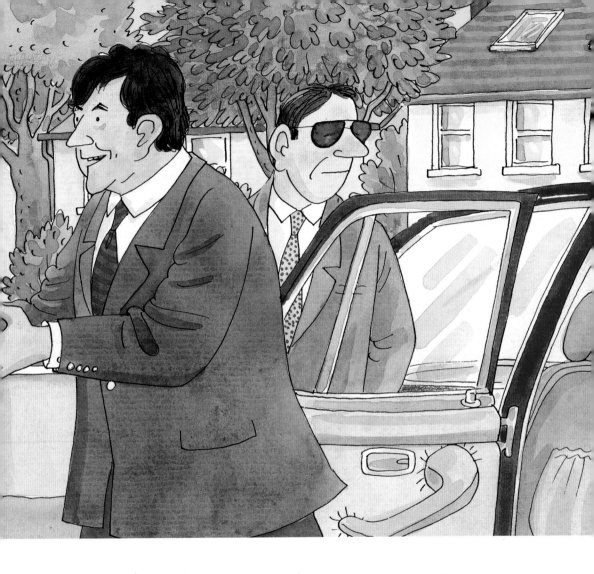

"It's my case," he said. "Thank you.
It was stolen. It is very important."

The man got in the car.

"Excuse me," said Wilma. "What is
in the case?"

"Ah!" said the man.
"My sandwiches."